MW00616167

PROCEDURE

Women Remaking Medicine
Vol. 1

Emily F. Peters

Connect with us:
hello@procedure.press
www.procedure.press

Instagram: @procedurepress
Twitter: @procedurepress

Soundtrack to this
volume on Spotify:
bit.ly/procedurevol1

Copyright © 2019 by Emily F. Peters

ISBN 978-0-578-41916-9

Library of Congress Cataloging-in-Publication Data is available upon request.

Cover design and illustration by Kellie Menendez
Book design by Blair Richardson, MiniSuper Studio
All photography by Larry Zhou, Studio Moot, except where noted
Page 13: image courtesy of the University of Virginia School of Nursing, photography by Melody Robbins
Page 34: photography by Nick Hagen
Page 46: image courtesy of the Dr. Susan Love Research Foundation
Page 88: photography by Judith Hill

Published by Procedure Press
www.procedure.press

An imprint of Uncommon Bold
www.uncommonbold.com
San Francisco, California

Printed in Canada

First printing, January 2019

Contents

She wrote a book

Emily F. Peters

Author, founder, brand strategist, survivor
San Francisco, California

Two years ago, medicine saved my life. Now, starting with this book, I thought I would do my part to help save medicine.

I'm no stranger to the millions of challenges, heartbreaks, and frustrations in America's healthcare system. The good news is that a million different problems mean there are also a million different ways to fix them. And a million different people whose voices we need to hear — specifically, yours.

Which is my not-so-secret mission behind creating *Procedure*. I want you to help. We need you!

This book tells the stories of women who are remaking medicine — a mix of perspectives from different roles in healthcare, different places, different generations, different backgrounds, and different paths. It is not an exaggeration to say that interviewing these women changed how I think about leadership and being a force for change in healthcare. More than one interview involved some light crying.

I hope you will find a bit of yourself in the profiles ahead. Maybe you're kind like Dorrie. Or brave like Esther. Or generous like Asha. Or a firebrand like Lisa. Or maybe you're someone completely different. These profiles show just a few of the many

ways to have an impact on healthcare by being exactly who you want to be. They demonstrate how medicine benefits from diversity, kindness, community, generosity, and creativity. How healthcare can benefit from someone just like you.

Me? I'm an advocate. My way of remaking medicine is listening, telling stories, and being a relentless campaigner for people doing good.

Personally, I am passionate about remaking medicine for women with stories like mine. In 2016, I came very, very close to dying during childbirth. With no warning, a serious hemorrhage meant I bled out just a few minutes after my daughter was born. While I was unconscious and my family had no idea if I was alive, I received 32 units of blood product (all the blood in my body nine times over), as well as a water balloon in my uterus, yards of gauze, and interventional radiology over the course of a few hours.

When I woke up in the ICU the next day, I was very sick but I also felt energized. I was alive! I had a beautiful baby daughter! All my family and friends were there! I got to meet new doctors and nurses every day! I got to watch the hospital at work! I almost immediately started thinking about how to frame my story, mentally taking notes of the details I saw and the impact it could have. It's a strange reaction, I realize, but it's very *me*.

Professionally, I've worked within the digital health sector for the last decade on new technologies designed to make patients healthier, providers happier, and medicine more affordable. It's been imperfect at times. It's also been rewarding to see fresh ideas help people. Along the way, I started a healthcare brand strategy studio called Uncommon Bold. Being CEO of your own company is terrific — I highly recommend it. You get to create your own policies and do things like decide to launch a book-publishing project.

There's a line in this book where Dr. Rana Awdish is recognized for her mix of "love and outrage" about healthcare. Isn't that perfect! I feel outrage. No one knows what caused my hemorrhage. We'll never know. My medical bills for that week in the hospital added up to more than half a million dollars. I was lucky to have been at a top hospital and in California where better policies have been enacted to address maternal health. I could very easily not have survived. The United States has the highest rate of maternal mortality in the industrialized world, with more than 50,000 women nearly dying in childbirth each year.

I also feel love. Medicine saved me. I loved the doctors and nurses who took care of me and fought hospital policies so my husband and baby could stay together with me in the ward. I loved getting back to work with my clients in the healthcare sector. A year later, the blood bank helped me arrange a meeting with some of the blood donors who saved my life. Seeing them and hearing my own doctor tearfully talk about my case...well, talk about love. That broke my heart into a thousand pieces in the best way possible.

Love and outrage, these are two powerful words. These two feelings together spark action. A million people (especially a million *women*) in healthcare with these feelings — that could be a revolution.

Why this book? Why women? Why now? I believe women are the secret to a better healthcare future. We're already almost 80 percent of the people working in the sector. And for the first time ever,

Acknowledgements

Thank you to my darling husband Rob, who is the best in every way. To my daughter, Lucy, who is so smart, strong, and brave. To my family and friends, who are everything.

Thank you to my generous helpers with this book project. Jaimy and Hemalee, who inspired it at the start. Christina, who saw what it could be and put in so much work. Kellie, who gave the book a cover and a soul with her art. Larry, who led photography. Meredith, who edited chapters from as far away as Oman. Blair, who designed the book so beautifully, so quickly. Lucy, the greatest proofreader. Greg and Lina, who read final drafts happily after I locked them in a cabin. Ashley, who put the word out. And, of course, all the women featured, who were each so generous with their time and supportive of the project.

Resources

A few resources we both thank and recommend:

- *Rock Health, especially their reporting on women in healthcare. Halle Tecco is an inspiration.*
- *Doximity's physician compensation report, which brings to light data on fair salaries and diversity gaps.*
- *The AMA's "organizational cost of physician burnout" calculator, which can help physicians understand their leverage with employers.*
- *The annual Women in the Workplace study from LeanIn.org and McKinsey & Company.*

women were the majority entering medical school in 2018. We are there, on the front lines, in every part of medicine, but very few of us are in leadership roles. There's not a single woman CEO of a Fortune 500 healthcare company. Only 11 percent of CEOs at the top 100 American hospitals are women. Women physicians also face a chasmic and increasing salary gap — earning an average of $105,000 a year less than equivalent men in 2017.

Women are ready, and there's plenty of work to be done. We can help fix the fundamental issues that have made our nation's healthcare system the most expensive in the world, while also far from the healthiest — and make the sector a better place to work for everyone.

So let's do it! Let's start companies. Let's speak up. Let's break through and be the first to do something. Let's make healthcare better for providers and patients. Let's make it more affordable. Let's share our stories. Let's write books. Let's remake medicine.

These women did it. I did it. So can you.

— **Emily F. Peters**

"
Love and outrage, these are two powerful words. These two feelings together spark action.
"

She built an empire of kindness

Dorrie Fontaine
RN, PhD, FAAN

Dean, educator, author, critical care nurse
Charlottesville, Virginia

Dorrie Fontaine may be the kindest person in healthcare. She is the model of how being mindful and generous and throwing birthday parties can help elevate you to the highest levels of leadership. She is so kind that one professor from her department went on to work for the Dalai Lama. As Dean of the School of Nursing at University of Virginia, she has graduated thousands of nurses, brought on more than 60 faculty members, and raised $25 million in grants and nearly $55 million in gifts and bequests for the program. As she prepares to retire, she is calling for others to carry her message of kindness in healthcare forward.

I'm so inspired by your work bringing kindness into healthcare and the reach of your career. This empire of people, organizations, and grants you've been able to build, as well as your focus on social and racial inequality. To me, you seem like a powerful person. Do you feel powerful?

That is so interesting that you would use that word. I don't think of myself as powerful. I think of myself as having a big impact, and that might be another way to define powerful. I've been a critical care nurse now for 46 years and in academia since 1978, and I've always looked at it as a way to have some amazing influence. If you have a good message, then you can watch people follow you. That extension of my work has been really, really rewarding because healthcare is so serious, and it's in a crisis.

How do you stay optimistic in a sector in crisis, where things often seem to be going badly?

I am very optimistic because I just happen to view the world that way, and I also see the amazing things that we can do. Certainly healthcare has gotten much tougher if we think about the people who are uninsured, if we think about burnout in healthcare, and how the electronic health record that we are trying so hard to make work often does not deliver on the promise that we expected. The challenges are all there. However, the fundamentally human instinct of caring for one another is still powerful.

You've talked about working to "reclaim the soul of healthcare." How do we do that?

Nurses and physicians go into healthcare because they want to make a difference. They love the thought of that patient-family contact and helping individuals. Then they get out into practice, and they're going, "Oh, goodness, I can't do all this. I could kill somebody. There are too many patients. Too much work."

"

I think of myself as
having a big impact, and
that might be another
way to define powerful.

"

They start to doubt themselves and they ask, "Did I really want to go into this? We can never do enough." Their souls start to get sapped. This is why we are working on a resilience initiative to restore people. Having them recall why they went into healthcare. Teaching them how they can look around and say, "This isn't right; here are the things that we can do to change it."

It is amazing to watch. We take 18-year-old nursing students and young medical students and help them to work together, rely on each other, and then most importantly, to take care of themselves. It's not selfish to take care of yourself. Yes, the patient is very, very important, as are the families. But if you don't put yourself on the list, then some tough things happen.

I like that you've talked about resilience as a kind of confidence in yourself as a provider. Resiliency is becoming a bit of a buzzword, and some health organizations are using it more in terms of getting providers to bounce back faster, to work more.

You are right to point that out. We have noticed that resiliency can be a two-edged sword. If we prepare people to take care of themselves — they are doing yoga, mindfulness, meditation, tai chi, and exercise — and then land in a workplace that is dysfunctional and chaotic, they will blame themselves, like, "Why can't I fix this?" What we are saying now is that we need compassionate organizations, compassionate institutions, and compassionate healthcare environments.

Resiliency is being your best self, but it is also not letting these hospitals off the hook. There is a real retention problem in nursing right now. People stay to that two-year point and then they go, "I'm out of here. This is too tough." I would love to have people band together, docs and nurses as well as other allied health professionals, and say, "Here are some ways we can fix healthcare," so that people look forward to going to work.

That relationship between physicians and nurses isn't always easy. In working on this book, I've been surprised by the reaction that nurses feel strongly that they're not part of "medicine," that

they're part of "healthcare." Do you view that tension between the professions as a missed opportunity?

I almost said something to you about, "Gee, it would be better if you called it healthcare." Nurses have felt for 150 years that we're perhaps under the thumb of medicine and physicians. We're two distinct professions; we're also each other's number one strategic partner. For years, I've been a big proponent of training people together so they have this understanding and a clear sense of each other's roles. Healthcare works best when people respect each other.

Of course, there will still be some mean nurses out there and some physicians who are demeaning and rude. It's possible that they're having a bad day. We have to get to know each other better. This new generation is beginning to have a much clearer idea of what it means to practice together in teams.

There's a theme here of needing institutional change. How have you been able to create an environment at UVA that breaks out of bad patterns?

I put a stake in the ground: "We need to be a place where people can come to work and look forward to being here, and where everyone is valued and can flourish." How can we make it better for everyone?

Right after I got here, I was invited by a benefactor to go to a place called Upaya, a Zen Buddhist retreat in Santa Fe. I was a brand-new dean. I first said, "No, I can't be doing this for eight days, with no cellphone, up in the mountains." I went with 15 people from here, and it was life changing. Mindfulness, meditation — it was all about being with dying. I'm an ICU nurse — 20 percent of our patients are dying every day in critical care. Stopping, focusing on your own ideas, attitudes, beliefs, and then recognizing the power within each of us to make a difference. It's what you say, it's how you treat people.

When I got back, I started bringing others. I've sent over 70 people to Upaya: doctors, nurses, chaplains, nutritionists, social

"

I've always
thought it's
okay to show
people that
you care
about them.

"

workers. At first, the faculty just thought, "This isn't right. What are we doing this for?" Gradually the students fell in love with it, and they would use what we taught them in the clinical setting. Taking a deep breath, grounding through their feet, and then going in the patient's room and focusing on the individual. Seeing the students, the faculty started to change their minds too and said, "You know, there is something to this." We started having a very generous spirit.

This all just seems so natural for you, so comfortable. Have you always found it easy to navigate and create change in healthcare?

I was never the best, or the smartest, or the one who was always the top. I just have always looked around and said, "Gee, how could we do this better?" I would kind of get out in front of things and say, "This doesn't seem right. Maybe we could think of another way." I wasn't grousing, complaining in the corner, and then quitting. I would stay and try to make things better, and from that, I would have a lot of people who wanted to join me. I have dear friends everywhere: University of Maryland, Georgetown, University of California San Francisco, and now here at UVA. This is the end of my career, but because I've mentored and helped so many people, I doubt that my work is stopping.

From working as a critical care nurse to fixing the culture of healthcare, it seems a consistent theme that you have a deep desire to heal things.

Yes, thank you. I feel like I've had the real privilege of being in places where there was always a need. When I first got to UVA to be the dean, people would say, "This is tough, and this is a big challenge — this is really awful." I looked at them; I don't know how this fell out of my mouth, but I said, "Well, I'm so glad I'm in a place where I'm needed."

I realized that there was a lot of opportunity to do some amazing things here. We've tripled applications, and we have tons of people who want to come work with us and teach with

> **I was never the best, or the smartest, or the one who was always the top. I just have always looked around and said, 'Gee, how could we do this better?'**

us because they heard it's a good environment. And now we're receiving the Healthy Work Environment Award from nursing's national honor society [Sigma] in 2019, just as I'm finishing up my deanship here. It's very heartwarming.

You talked about helping providers to be empathetic, to keep their compassion and their humanity. We often hear stories of training and work doing the opposite, of stripping that away. How do you keep that going?

I've always thought it's okay to show people that you care about them. It helps. It does make them feel special. I try to recognize people in positive ways and try to remember people's names. When I would teach class, I would work hard to learn people's names. It's not that hard to do. It brings people joy.

We're trying to have people look at how special they can really be, because these are tough jobs. We're not preparing people to sit in a corner and think about Shakespeare. They will be facing life and death. We have to role model a lot. Many years ago, a wonderful colleague said to me, "The last thing we should be doing is harming their self-esteem." There are so many good ways to help people be their best selves, and that's what we're trying to do here. That's what I'm trying to do in all sorts of venues.

One of those venues is your own house on the "Lawn," a UNESCO World Heritage Site where select faculty live at the center of UVA. You've turned that facility into a real home, with parties, dinners, and receptions. I read you've hosted over 100 birthday parties for faculty and staff from the School of Nursing. Why do you take that kind of fun so seriously?

There has to be some time to get to know each other, even in these busy clinical and academic settings. Some kind of social time, whether it's after work, or it's lunch in the staff lounge where everybody gets to participate. It is so important. How can people come together and get to know each other, understand each other, and say thank you?

I think we would be in a better place in the world if more people followed your advice. Do you have a single thing you tell graduates or people who are trying to follow in your model in healthcare to stay focused on?

Have a generous spirit. Reach out to others. Look the patient in the eyes. Hold a hand. Greet every single person. The most important thing is that human connection.

> Have a generous spirit. Reach out to others. Look the patient in the eyes. Hold a hand. Greet every single person. The most important thing is that human connection.

She fostered communities

Asha S. Collins
PhD

Scientist, strategist, investor
South San Francisco, California

Asha Collins is transforming the way new medications are tested as head of U.S. country clinical operations for Genentech. Her job is focused on innovative ways to deliver clinical trials to communities, but her belief in people goes far beyond the lab bench. A scientist at heart and cancer biologist by training, she has seen the influence of community in every step of her journey from Detroit, to the National Institute of Health, to Ethiopia, and ultimately, Silicon Valley. Today, she is also an angel investor at Pipeline Angels, a mentor with Backstage Capitol, and advisor to CircleOf, a care community startup. She is never done connecting people.

Every biologist I know seems to have a favorite organism that they can geek out on for an hour. What is yours?

Herpes viruses! I studied them for so long. They've often helped me across the many different therapeutic areas that I've been involved in. There's so many connections between herpes, us, and disease. There's so much viral DNA in our own DNA that it's not clear what would happen if we didn't have that anymore. The entire herpes virology family is a great dinner topic conversation. Which is why virologists are not invited to dinner parties as much as we should be.

That's a shame! Were you a herpes-enthusiast from the very start?

When I was growing up, I first wanted to be a geophysicist because I was in love with earthquakes and the earth itself. I always loved science and math. I've always been excited about the scientific process. I wasn't one of those kids who did tons of experiments in the kitchen, but I read voraciously. I had a high curiosity and a full imagination. I would go off into these worlds of my own in my books and in my mind. I grew up in a very large extended family, but I also was an only child. That time alone is when my imagination was allowed to expand.

Did that extended family help turn you into a scientist?

I was born in Detroit, on the East Side, and went to Detroit public schools. I grew up in the '80s during the crack epidemic. There was a lot of devastation in those urban areas. Detroit was already hit hard by the post-manufacturing wave. Those two things together had a significant negative impact on the city.

It was a really loving environment for me, though. My mom was a single mom. We lived on the very same block that she grew up on. My grandmother and my great uncle, her brother, lived in a duplex in the middle of that block. At the other end, two of my great aunts lived in another duplex. On that one single block there were three generations of family. While there was a lot going on in Detroit, I was in a very nurturing environment and felt very safe. It gave me a broader sense of family and network and community in a way that is still super important to me. Community is very sacred to me.

It sounds like there was a whole community on that block trying to lift you up and push you out into the world on a different path.

Many of my uncles and aunts have middle school educations. My grandmother was illiterate. Many of the people around me did not have college educations, and many of them didn't even have high school educations. I was pushed forward. I was given space to go in the corner and read my books. There were so many people giving me space and opportunity and sacrificing for me and protecting me so that I could be my little nerdy self.

My mom drove me to manners school, for example. No one I knew growing up went to manners school. She had the foresight to think, "I don't know what all these forks and spoons are about, but I want my daughter to know about this, and I'm going to drive to get her there every weekend to make sure that she has it."

A lot of my motivation is to make sure that their sacrifice isn't for naught.

What does your family think of your work with Genentech now?

Genentech is a lot easier to explain than when I was at the lab as a scientist. No one really knows what a scientist does. Now, I say I work on clinical trials. "We test new medicines."

My main focus is developing the clinical trial operations of the future. And we can do that by leveraging our juxtaposition to Silicon Valley, which is a hub of innovation for the world. We can leverage the technology and the brain trust of this area — literally the people who our kids go to school with, who we go to synagogue with, exercise with, hike with, and go to dinner with on the weekend here — to push forward how we do clinical trials today.

Understanding the dynamics of the demographic shift in the U.S. is part of that. With the rise of AI, personalized medicine, and the evolution of treatments for smaller and smaller patient segments, we need to make sure that our clinical trial populations are representative. We can't just include people of one certain race or people of one certain background in clinical trials. Being as inclusive as possible brings us into the 21st century and sets us up for success in the future.

For outsiders like myself who've never worked in a big Fortune 500 organization, it can seem very impersonal. However, it sounds like part of your work is building those communities inside of Genentech.

One of my first priorities at Genentech was to strengthen the community in our part of the organization. For me, culture and community are a key part of laying the foundation for progress.

> ❝ Community is very sacred to me. ❞

As a whole, Genentech really understands this — that people, all people, are key to the success of our business.

When I was in the interview process here, they invited me to an event for Black History Month. I've been to so many of these things before, but this stood out. It was amazing in the diversity of black leaders that they showcased. The leaders were diverse in their own right in terms of their background, in terms of communication style, where they were from, in terms of their thinking style. The event also showcased Genentech's involvement in a number of community programs and that their success was dependent and interwoven with the success of the people in their surrounding

> My first strategy is to understand and be comfortable with the fact that I don't have all the answers, I don't always know what I'm doing, I don't necessarily know what I should be doing. It is okay to not know or to not be sure. If I'm doing the things that I've always done, that I know how to do, then I wouldn't be growing. I wouldn't be happy because I wouldn't be growing.

community. Those two things together made me want to be a part of Genentech even more. I had never felt that before in a company.

That sounds amazing. Are there other ways that Genentech stands out to you as different from other places you've worked?

In previous roles, if I needed a breather, or if I needed to pull myself together, I could always go to the women's bathroom because there would be very few people in there. That's not the case at Genentech. There are women in the bathroom all the time because there are women all across the organization. It's great. However, I do miss having that space for myself.

Your career has moved forward so quickly. I'm sure there have been harder times and times that you were hitting a roadblock. What's your strategy for navigating through those things?

My first strategy is to understand and be comfortable with the fact that I don't have all the answers, I don't always know what I'm doing, I don't necessarily know what I should be doing. It is okay to not know or to not be sure. If I'm doing the things that I've always done, that I know how to do, then I wouldn't be growing. I wouldn't be happy because I wouldn't be growing.

The other thing that I'm exploring more is to really understand the source of the obstacles. To be curious about them. Is this an obstacle that I'm making up in my mind? Or is this actually a roadblock for me? Being curious about why I feel stuck. Having people to talk through that with is always helpful because many times I can't get unstuck by myself. Even if they have different perspectives than me, and I decide to go with my perspective and not theirs, I'm in that much stronger a position because then I know why I'm not taking the alternative path.

Both of those are such scientific approaches. It's all about hypotheses and researchers and co-authors. It's so ingrained for you!

You're right! The science never goes away.

What did your "advisors" think when you decided to go to Ethiopia to help build a clinical research center focused on mental health studies? Was it kind of on a whim?

I was a consultant at the time and flying constantly. On one flight, I chatted with the person next to me who turned out to be the lead on global psychiatry at Harvard [David C. Henderson, MD, now at Boston University]. We had an awesome conversation about behavior change, me speaking from the organization level and him from an individual level. A year later, we met up in Cambridge, and he invited me to join his team in Addis Ababa setting up a clinical trials unit. My mother and my husband were like, "I'm sorry, you're going *where*? You met a man on a plane and now you're going to go to Ethiopia with him?"

It was difficult, and it was amazingly rewarding, too. We think the conditions in the U.S. are difficult for people with mental health issues. Working with this team gave me better appreciation of the spectrum of hardships that people with mental illness across the world face. Many times it was heartbreaking to see how people were being mistreated — all because of mental health issues. The people who are working to close that gap in understanding are angelic, heroic in the work that they're doing ceaselessly. That experience changed how I saw my place in the world.

It also showed me opportunities because I saw some of the progressive parts of Ethiopia's healthcare system. Local community clinics there had their results posted, written in marker, the number of patients they'd seen that month and year, the number of different indications that they had treated, and their outcomes. We don't have that in our hospitals in America today. Also, because there is no large technology infrastructure there, we could quickly put in innovative systems. We're held back in the West by all these long-standing healthcare infrastructure pieces that are really hard to extricate and change. In Ethiopia, we could leapfrog the West and create a definitive view of what clinical trials in the future look like.

Another way you're trying to leapfrog healthcare ahead is through angel investment. How did you get involved in the startup world?

> **No matter where you are or what's happening, treating people respectfully is the most important thing. People are valuable. People are the value.**

I came kicking and screaming to the Bay Area from New York with my husband. Once I got over myself, I thought, "We have this short amount of time where I'm in Silicon Valley. What can I do here that's unique? How can I make the most of this experience?" I was thinking about my corporate athleticism. I work in huge organizations and want to understand what it takes to succeed in these smaller companies, too. The idea of being able to invest in startups and see what it takes for them to succeed came across my desk through Pipeline Angels.

I focused on providing initial money to women in STEM and helping social entrepreneurs. I started understanding how my experience at these large companies and my scientific background could contribute to helping small businesses and startups to see a broader future and grow in scale. I love the energy. I love working with them. I love connecting people.

Sounds like you've built yet another community around you. Is building communities your superpower?

Relationships are so important to me. Especially as I'm thinking more about the partnership between humans and technology and the value that humans bring. Healthcare is a small place. The world's a very small place, so treat people well in every situation. No matter where you are or what's happening, treating people respectfully is the most important thing. People are valuable. People are the value. ◼

She lived to tell her story

Rana Awdish

MD, FCCP

Critical care physician, educator, author, painter
Detroit, Michigan

On the final day of her three-year pulmonary and critical care fellowship training at Detroit's Henry Ford Hospital, Rana Awdish became a critical care patient herself. Seven months pregnant, she bled to death in the operating room of her own hospital. The baby was lost. She was brought back to life. Her experience of being a patient changed everything she thought she knew about illness. Ten years later, she published a book about her story. *In Shock* became a bestseller, sparking conversations around the world about compassionate care.

If your story wasn't true, it would seem totally implausible. That this happened the last day of your training in critical care medicine. At your own hospital. And then your first patient on your first day back at work had the same syndrome they thought you had....

It was unbelievable. There were so many moments like that for me, as if some larger force had a hand in things. That first patient, who was essentially a static replica of me from six months prior, felt like a reminder in some ways of how far I had come and how much I had to be grateful for.

How did you know when you were ready to go back to work?

I really mentally needed to go back. I had become my only patient. I was obsessing about everything that was still wrong in my body, in my own labs, and my plodding recovery. I started to feel that it was unhealthy, that I needed to get out of my own head, and I was willing to push myself physically to do that. It was a difficult transition, but I was surrounded by a lot of people who made it easier. At first, I couldn't drive myself to work. My colleagues would pick me up. Sometimes I would have to take naps in the call room.

But it was important for my healing to feel of use. The illness had taken so much away from me. I wasn't willing to give it my career, too. I was going to have agency about it and say, "No, you've taken enough. This is where it stops."

What has this process of writing and publicizing your story been like?

I didn't go into this thinking that I was going to write a book. I started speaking about my experiences in small ways, such as giving grand rounds at the hospital. A video of me speaking at Sepsis Day started circulating on the internet and made it into the hands of a literary agent, Jacqueline Murphy at InkWell in Boston. She messaged me and said, "I saw your video. You have a story to tell. I don't know if you've thought about writing a book, but if you want to, I will help you." As I was writing, I started to have this appreciation of, "Oh my gosh, there's so much content here. I'm fortunate to have had this experience to draw from. I don't want to waste it and not write it well." You only die so many times.

Your story seems to have struck a nerve in healthcare. Was the book well received?

Shockingly well. I worried that the book would be something people would reject, especially in medicine. That they wouldn't want to admit this was who we were. The reception has been just the opposite. It has been so welcoming.

I think the value of the book comes from the fact that it is creating safe spaces in the world for people to talk about things that are really difficult to discuss, that we don't allow ourselves to talk about as often as we probably should.

American healthcare is going through some tough questions right now around what is good medicine. I love the quote one of your book reviewers wrote that your perspective is a combination of "love and outrage," which I think is so true for many of us in healthcare.

It's a constant tug, isn't it? I revered medicine as a profession from when I was a kid. I wanted to be a part of it, and then you look behind the curtain and you realize, "There are things here I'm ashamed of. How do I reconcile this love and outrage?" The only way I found I could reconcile that is to try to create change.

Why did you choose critical care medicine, working in intensive care with patients facing life-threatening conditions?

I did my residency training in New York with these amazingly inspiring critical care physicians who drew me into it. Critical care to me was the most medicine-y medicine that you could get. It was all the organs failing, so you had to be a complete doctor. I couldn't have gone into any other field. I cared too much about all the other organs to leave them behind.

> **❝**
>
> Why were we only focused on learning diseases and treatments if the vulnerability of patients and their need for human connection was so much more important than we were ever taught?
>
> **❞**

I would get to intersect with people at these really critical junctures in their life when they were either going to get better with care that was really intensive, or they were going to progress toward death. It was a journey that I would be a part of facilitating, and it seemed important to me and serious in a way that I admired.

How did your illness change the way you thought about healthcare and your role as a physician?

I had to unpack the reasons why we got to where we are in medicine. When I was looking at the things that hurt me during my illness, hospitalizations, and surgery, I never would have thought I was the type of person who would have been hurt by those things. Hearing physicians say I was "trying to die on them"

"

I don't think we have reached the tipping point yet where physicians and patients understand that if we banded together, we would have so much power.

"

or that I was "circling the drain." As a physician, I thought that if the medicine went well, the rest of it was less important, squishy, soft. What was shocking was the vulnerability of being a patient and how immediately it changes your sense of agency within your world, your sense of need for human care. This realization was so different than anything I had expected, it made me wonder why we were training doctors the way we were training them. Why were we only focused on learning diseases and treatments if the vulnerability of patients and their need for human connection was so much more important than we were ever taught?

I worry we're teaching medical students and residents to fall in love with diseases and not with their patients. We're not giving them the tools they need to develop relationships that are nurturing in a bi-directional way, where you can shepherd a patient along a journey; where you're meeting their goals and helping to facilitate the process in a way that nurtures you, too; and where you feel of use. I worry we're creating technicians who are cut off from the most life-sustaining forces that are part of being a physician.

Many, many medical students have only ever experienced health. Their parents may have only ever experienced health, and illness is this whole other world to them. There is a lot of privilege, honestly. Not just socioeconomic privilege, but health privilege. I want medical students to have grit. There is suffering and you can sit with it and it is okay. You can't always heal, but your presence can be healing.

There is so much talk today around things like replacing doctors with AI and chatbots. To me, this buzz is a fundamental misunderstanding of the value that physicians bring to patients. Do you see a future where we could carve out a little more space for valuing the empathy that comes with being a "healer" within this technology evolution?

Absolutely. I think that balance of empathy and technology is the holy grail. That is what was promised to us with electronic medical records: that much of the burden of documentation would be taken away by this fabulous new shiny system. That we would be allowed to be healers. It's been the opposite. It has turned us into this interface between medicine and documentation. Wouldn't it be wonderful if technology helped us document our exams automatically with AI and our conversations were coded instantly for insurance so we didn't have to type out notes or dictate them later?

I'm often frustrated that doctors — this population of incredibly smart, forceful, powerful, intelligent people — don't feel agency in being able to change and fix problems in medicine. By virtue of your illness and this book, you stumbled into realizing the power that individual physicians have to create change. Why do you think we are in a place with healthcare where a lot of people feel powerless?

One of the unfortunate truths is that we abdicated our responsibility as physicians. We told ourselves for so long that our gifts lie in the medicine, the science, and the healing, and that the business of medicine is something anyone could do. We could offload the business side. We gave away our power when we did that. Now medicine has become a business, and we are employees of that business. I don't think we have reached the tipping point yet where physicians and patients understand that if we banded together, we would have so much power.

What's next for you? It feels to me like the world is ready for you to do something bigger.

Oh, thank you. It is the hippie yoga person in me who wants to follow where the path leads, and I don't try to presuppose too much on what's next. Right now, I get to occupy this space where I'm inspiring others to effect change in their own communities.

One thing I did feel guilty about when *In Shock* was done was that I very deliberately didn't identify as a female physician in the book. I felt that the best way of having my voice heard was not to overly identify as a female and over-identified as a physician. Women's voices are discredited in a lot of ways, especially

"

I want medical students to have grit. There is suffering and you can sit with it and it is okay. You can't always heal, but your presence can be healing.

"

in illness narratives. People have commented that there's less emotion around the loss of the pregnancy than they would've expected, that I seem cold and certainly distant at some points in the book. I think that's true, and that was almost deliberate because I bought into the myth that to be a valuable voice, I couldn't be overly feminine. That makes me angry, that I subverted my agency in that way and bought into that myth. At the same time, it's been redemptive because the community embracing *In Shock* is female.

There are more women going into medical school than ever before. As a group, we are saying medicine will be better if it looks more like us. This is powerful, and it is something we didn't allow ourselves to say because we were tokens in the system for so long. There are now enough of us that we can shape medical culture. A physician looks like somebody who does yoga, who paints, and who enjoys cooking. I want us as doctors to accept that there are different phenotypes and to show others this is what a physician looks like. A physician can make time for self-care. A physician doesn't have to burn out before they find something powerful that rejuvenates them.

> **Don't change to fit medicine. Let it change to fit you because you're healthier and more whole than medicine is right now. Don't meet it where it is, pull it toward you.**

That has been a journey for me, of realizing how much power female physicians have right now to change medicine in their image. What I tell medical students all the time is, "Don't change to fit medicine. Let it change to fit you because you're healthier and more whole than medicine is right now. Don't meet it where it is, pull it toward you."

What else do you want to change in medicine?

The epidemic of physician suicide is very much on my mind. I wrote in the book about two of the suicides of my interns when I was in residency. That was probably the chapter hardest for me to write about because I had a lot of shame in seeing the warning signs I hadn't heeded.

We have to show up for ourselves. We have to show up for each other. When people are suffering, whether it is patients or our colleagues, we need to believe in the power of our presence to just sit with somebody and say, "I don't have a solution. I don't know what to say right now, but I am going to sit here with you and just be present." That kind of holding space for somebody, it is something that I think can save more lives than we know. ◖

She did what she wanted

Susan Love

MD, MBA

Surgeon, researcher, author, activist
Encino, California

Susan Love is comfortable not fitting in. She was the first person in her family to finish college. In the 1970s, she became the first woman general surgeon at Boston's Beth Israel Hospital. A pioneer in LGBTQ rights, she took a landmark case to the Supreme Court of Massachusetts in 1993 that led to the legalization of second-parent adoptions. A "founding mother" of the breast cancer advocacy movement in the 1990s, she forever changed diagnosis and treatment for millions of women. Surviving her own cancer inspired her to reach even further.

As an outsider, how did you keep breaking through over and over again?

In some ways, it was very useful being an outsider. I was a woman, and then I was an out lesbian woman. I knew they weren't going to like me anyway, so who cares? I learned the power of being an outsider, which is really the power that you have nothing to lose.

Even though it seems like those were harder times for women back in the 1970s, it was easier for me. There are now a number of women who are department heads in medicine, and there are very strong women in medicine groups on Twitter. In some ways, women in medicine today may not be as free to just do what they think should be done because there is more to lose. When you are a surgeon and nobody wants to offer you a job, then you just do it your own way.

Where does that comfort with being an outsider come from?

It is partly my personality and partly because we moved around a lot when I was young. When we moved to Puerto Rico, I was the only person in my middle school class who was from the mainland.

You tried becoming a nun during medical school because it was a clear path toward leadership in healthcare at the time. This was an established way of pursuing a medical career, but it wasn't the way that you wanted to do it?

In those days, as a nun, you had many more options. You could be head of a hospital, you could run a university, you could be a doctor researching out in the field. I fleetingly went into the convent for about nine months. It was quickly clear that being a nun was not for me. You had to put up with a lot of boundaries and rules and regulations.

How did you feel going into medical school at a time when quotas kept the rate of women students extremely low?

After the convent, I went back to finish at Fordham University and then went to medical school at SUNY Downstate in Flatbush. At the time, most medical schools had five percent quotas for admitting women. Downstate allowed in 10 percent; they were considered very liberal. I got honors in surgery in medical school. When I met the chief of surgery, he said, "Well, I don't think women should be surgeons."

I managed to get a good residency in Boston regardless. I trained as a surgeon at Beth Israel Hospital in Boston, which is part of Harvard. It was quite a remarkable time. Patients would pat you on the butt when you walked by. You'd be scrubbing your hands to go into surgery, and you couldn't touch anybody, and then somebody would come by and run their hand down your ass. You'd walk into the operating room, and they'd say, "Is the surgeon here yet?"

I finished and I was chief resident, and then nobody offered me a job. Usually, when you're a chief resident at one of the Harvard hospitals, you get heavily recruited. Nobody wanted a woman.

So I started a practice and waited. The patients who were sent to me and those who found me were women with breast issues. A lot of people think I became a breast surgeon because I had a personal experience or a case in my own family. Actually, it was just sexism. Those were the patients I could get.

How did you turn that focus on breast cancer into an advantage?

By chance, there was much more data and science to go by in breast cancer than in many other of the cancer fields. In that sense, it was really encouraging. I found that I could explain breast cancer well to people, and my practice bloomed. In 1990, I wrote the *Breast Book,* now in its sixth edition. That was the first time there was a book explaining the science of cancer directly to people. That really carried my career further.

When did you decide to use the popularity of the book to build something even more impactful for women?

"

I learned the
power of being
an outsider,
which is really
the power
that you have
nothing to lose.

"

I was giving a lot of talks when the book first came out. It was at one long conference where I was looking for a laugh. I said, "I don't know what it's going to take to eradicate breast cancer. Maybe we should just march topless on the White House." Everybody laughed because the vision of all these topless women marching on George H. W. Bush was indeed comical. Afterwards, they came up to me and said, "When do we leave?" I realized the time had come to politicize breast cancer.

That was the beginning of the National Breast Cancer Coalition, which is still around today. We lobbied to have the money for one B-1 bomber go to breast cancer. It was an election year,

I said, 'I don't know what it's going to take to eradicate breast cancer. Maybe we should just march topless on the White House.' Everybody laughed because the vision of all these topless women marching on George H. W. Bush was indeed comical. Afterwards, they came up to me and said, 'When do we leave?'

and it was right after Anita Hill and the hearings for Clarence Thomas. All these people in Congress were trying to do something good for women so they didn't look like such jerks. Breast cancer wasn't so political as, say, abortion or birth control, so we got the funds.

I continued to practice in Boston. I came out publicly as a lesbian in the *Boston Globe* and then subsequently had a child with my partner Helen. Two lesbians having a kid was not seen in those days. I've always done what I wanted with my life.

After starting the first all-women breast center in Boston, and then moving to California and starting the Revlon/UCLA Breast Center, you briefly worked on the business side of medicine. What was that like?

I got a business degree at UCLA Anderson School of Management and started three medical device companies. One made money and two didn't. We developed a way that you could look at fluid from the breast ducts, almost like a pap smear of the breast to look for abnormal cells. That company was bought by a mammography company just so they could kill it. It disillusioned me to the business world. So I started a nonprofit, which is what I do now.

You were diagnosed with acute myeloid leukemia after a routine blood test in 2012 and came close to dying. How did that experience of being a cancer patient change your perspective?

It certainly made me feel more urgency. It also made me realize how important it was to try to get other people involved. Trying not to do it all myself. If something happens to me, the project, or the questions we're working on, all this progress won't just die with me. I'm figuring out how best to mentor and encourage the younger generation of women in healthcare. Over the last couple of years, I realized more and more the need for champions — people who can help, who can guide, and can say, "You're doing fine. Keep going."

What are you working on currently with the Dr. Susan Love Research Foundation?

We're trying to figure out breast cancer so we can end it. One of the things I'm obsessed with is the anatomy of the breast. We're working on mapping the anatomy of the breast, how many holes are on the nipple, where the breast ducts are, because we actually don't know. We don't have a map. Breast cancer starts in the milk duct; if we had a map, it could be really useful.

We're also doing a lot of work around "collateral damage." We've come a long way in treating cancer. Consequences of treatment have been called "side effects," but side effects really are transient, and collateral damage is forever. It is sort of like your car being in a crash. You can have it repaired, but the passenger door never closes the same way again. After having a cancer experience, and all this poison and chemo, you definitely have collateral damage.

Instead of using "patient-reported outcomes," which are questionnaires written by doctors and researchers for patients to fill out and usually miss most of the important things, we decided to just ask people. We're acknowledging the collateral damage — not just the physical, but also of quality of life and psycho-social. Even with metastatic breast cancer, which we can't cure, we are keeping people alive a lot longer. We want the quality of their life to be as good as possible.

Part of the Foundation is an "Army of Women" you've assembled who are volunteering to participate in research studies. Where did you get that idea?

So much breast cancer research has been done on mice and rats. Ten years ago, we asked, "Why aren't you doing these studies on people?" Researchers said, "Well, we don't know how to find women." I did. Now we have a network of over 350,000 women who are willing to be in studies. Researchers who are looking for people to study come to us, and we send the opportunity to participate in their studies out to everybody. Even if you may not fit the study, your sister who lives in Chicago may be perfect. By sending it out to everybody, the opportunities get virally sent further.

You've been able to have such a positive impact on healthcare in your career. What's your advice for others in the field who want to create change?

People in medicine today shouldn't think, "Oh, this is the way it is always going to be" because it is not the way it always is going to be. This is the way it always *has been*, and you can change it. You can either change it from the inside or from the outside. Women don't get enough encouragement to do that. We get too much of the "be a good little girl" thing. Figure out how you think medicine could be better and do it. The worst thing that will happen is you will fail; it won't be the first time, and it won't be the last time, and nobody will die if you try to change the system. ◣

> This is the way it always *has been,* and you can change it. You can either change it from the inside or from the outside.

She went straight to the source

Lisa Bari

MBA, MPH

Health policy innovator
Baltimore, Maryland

Lisa Bari had a dream marketing career in Silicon Valley. For a decade, she worked with high-profile brands including Art.com and Virgin America. When she joined Practice Fusion, an electronic health record startup, she realized how much healthcare needed her help. She then earned a master's at the Harvard T.H. Chan School of Public Health and went straight to work for the federal government. Now at the Center for Medicare and Medicaid Innovation (the Innovation Center), she is leading major changes to improve patient care while reducing cost in the world's most expensive healthcare system.

After working at Practice Fusion and training at Harvard, were you surprised still to see the extent of the issues in our healthcare system when you started work from the policy side?

I already had a sense that it was going to be bad. The depths of the bad, though...yes, I still manage to be surprised by how far down it goes. How it seems like there's no place in healthcare that isn't tainted by this endless drive for new, creative, and terrible ways to make money.

Do you wish you could just rip out and replace our healthcare system with one of the other models you've seen around the world?

Every healthcare system has its own unique set of problems. I hesitate to compare because every country should be able to build a healthcare system that matches their particular values, their particular laws, and the things that they care about. When I lived outside of the United States, it gave me perspective on how deeply I care about American values. I care about things being fair. I care about having no monarchy. I care about our democratic values.

If you take a deep look at the values of the people in our country, I don't think they match the healthcare system we have today. Americans believe in fairness, we believe in transparency, we believe in competition, but we don't see those things in our healthcare system. It's not an even playing field. You can't find out what a procedure is going to cost before you go to the hospital. You don't have fair prices for medications. The fact that you could be passed out in a hospital and charged thousands of dollars for an out-of-network anesthesiologist is unconscionable. That is not fair.

Let's actually create a healthcare system that matches our values. These things need to change.

Is that what you're working on at the Innovation Center?

We are testing innovative ways to pay for and deliver care. That's powerful. Having that kind of big impact is what attracted me to working in the government. I keep health equity in mind in my work every day. I try to implement policies that will make life better for people.

The gains and benefits of technology have not been equally distributed in our country and across the world. What are the things that I can do as a healthcare policy professional to help change that? To move in a direction where the benefits of technology, especially health technology, reach as many people as possible. That's my north star.

As a civil servant, I know that I am working to serve Medicare and Medicaid beneficiaries. That is a role I take seriously.

You don't hear that job description much these days. Why is calling yourself a "civil servant" important to you?

I think it's a big distinction. I, and many of my colleagues, hold the mission of serving the American people really dear. We use it to motivate ourselves. It's not always easy to work in the government. People are criticizing you all the time; it can be turbulent. If you have that mission of serving the American people in mind, it helps keep you motivated.

Where does your sense of duty — of being a good, engaged citizen — come from?

Both of my parents were labor organizers. My mother was an environmental activist. I grew up with this idea that it was important to stand up for what you believe in. There are pictures of me as a little child leading a protest to protect an endangered redwood forest. There are letters to the editor from me when I was a very young person. In middle school, I wrote a letter to the school paper about a perceived act of sexism in an article, saying, "This is sexist and wrong, and we should condemn this." That was me.

I'm not afraid to speak truth to power. I'm not afraid to stand up for what I believe in. I'm not afraid to call something out.

I'd like to think that I do it in a way that is constructive and respectful. That is something that definitely has followed me everywhere I have worked.

Office environments can be a tough place to speak out. How do you put that kind of activism to work in your career?

The way I lead is to make sure there is space for different ideas. I make sure to call out things I think maybe aren't true or situations where we are not living up to the values we espouse. Sometimes you'll have a meeting where the leader or manager is saying something that maybe five or six people in the room know is not true. In many cases, people are afraid to speak up or are afraid to voice their opinions.

I generally try to speak up, and I try to open up space for people to be heard. I'm willing to take the fall for other people to be able to speak.

You have to get involved as a citizen if you care about healthcare.

"

Americans believe in fairness, we believe in transparency, we believe in competition, but we don't see those things in our healthcare system.

"

How can people best speak up about our healthcare system today?

You have to get involved as a citizen if you care about healthcare. That can be engaging with your elected officials. It can be getting involved in a free clinic in your neighborhood. It can be running for office. It can be advocating for patients. There is a whole variety of ways you can get involved as a citizen and a voter. That is the only way democracy works.

I recently spoke to a small business owner who got involved with his local hospital and is now on the board. Bringing in people who aren't healthcare insiders can especially help because they can say, "This doesn't make sense! Why are we doing it this way? Why would we charge this much? Why do we expect this kind of treatment? Why don't we know what something costs?" These are reasonable questions that real people can ask. We need to ask those questions.

What's your realistically optimistic prediction for where American healthcare will be in 10 years? Paint us a picture of the future, when we'll have rocket cars and affordable healthcare.

My dream for the future is that we are completely broken away from the fee-for-service payment model. Various organizations are taking on financial risk for their patients, and they are doing everything they can do to make sure people are healthy from the beginning.

That means people are getting substantial preventive healthcare. Healthcare organizations are working on social determinants of health: making sure people have enough food, that they are getting enough exercise, they are well vaccinated, they are getting enough sleep, their stress is lowered. We will have turned our focus toward keeping people healthy versus trying to duct-tape today's system where people are already so sick, and there's so much burden on patients and their families.

We are certainly going to see a major leap forward in cures. The key will be how we make these treatments affordable to everybody. We have to figure out a way to pay for it. The way we

"

I'm not afraid to speak truth to power. I'm not afraid to stand up for what I believe in. I'm not afraid to call something out. I'd like to think that I do it in a way that is constructive and respectful.

"

can do that is by transforming our system away from fee-for-service and really truly moving toward value-based care.

There is so much waste in the healthcare system today. We can pay for the changes we need if we find ways to get rid of that waste and make things flow more freely. I don't know how else we can move forward; it is not tenable. There is no more money. We can't keep paying what we're paying and continue to not get value out of it. We have the worst health outcomes in the developed world, with the highest prices by far. We just can't keep going down this path.

There will always be winners and losers, but my dream for the healthcare future is that the winners are patients and their families.

I've known you for a long time, and I've been pushing you to run for office for almost as long. I'm very pleased you're starting to sound like a campaigner here.

I can tell you that running for office has never been my plan. I'm focused on the work I'm doing right now. Am I going to say, "No, never" though? Of course not.

Spoken like a true congresswoman.

Someday, Emily. Someday. ◣

She raised her voice

Esther Choo
MD, MPH

Emergency medicine physician, researcher, activist, founder
Portland, Oregon

Esther Choo didn't know she was going to be famous when she sent out a couple tweets before going to work an overnight ER shift. Reacting to the deadly white supremacist rally in Charlottesville the day before, she posted a short thread about showing compassion whenever a patient in Oregon refuses treatment from her because she is Asian. When she logged in to Twitter again after work, the story had taken off. Her original post would be retweeted 25,000 times, and the story was soon covered by media around the world. More than 40,000 followers later, she is now a powerful global voice for equity in medicine.

Esther Choo MD MPH ✓
@choo_ek

1/ We've got a lot of white nationalists in Oregon. So a few times a year, a patient in the ER refuses treatment from me because of my race.

2:46 PM - 13 Aug 2017

24,646 Retweets 47,160 Likes

💬 2.4K ⟲ 25K ♡ 47K

Esther Choo MD MPH ✓ @choo_ek · 13 Aug 2017
2/ I don't get angry or upset, just incredulous over the psychology of it. The conversation usually goes like this...
💬 31   ⟲ 1.8K   ♡ 9.0K

Esther Choo MD MPH ✓ @choo_ek · 13 Aug 2017
3/ Me: "I understand your viewpoint. I trained at elite institutions & have been practicing for 15 years. You are welcome to refuse care...
💬 21   ⟲ 1.8K   ♡ 8.7K

Esther Choo MD MPH ✓ @choo_ek · 13 Aug 2017
4/ ... under my hands, but I feel confident that I am the most qualified to care for you. Especially since the alternative is an intern."
💬 31   ⟲ 1.8K   ♡ 9.0K

Esther Choo MD MPH ✓ @choo_ek · 13 Aug 2017
5/ And they invariably pick the intern, as long as they are white. Or they leave. Breathtaking, isn't it? To be so wedded to your theory ...
💬 52   ⟲ 2.0K   ♡ 11K

Esther Choo MD MPH ✓ @choo_ek · 13 Aug 2017
6/ ... of white superiority, that you will bet your life on it, even in the face of clear evidence to the contrary?
💬 58   ⟲ 2.0K   ♡ 11K

Esther Choo MD MPH ✓ @choo_ek · 13 Aug 2017
7/ Sometimes I just look at them, my kin in 99.9% of our genetic code, and fail to believe they don't see our shared humanity.
💬 40   ⟲ 2.6K   ♡ 15K

Esther Choo MD MPH ✓ @choo_ek · 13 Aug 2017
8/ You know what gives me hope? A few get uncomfortable and apologize in the same breath they refuse to let me treat them. You see...
💬 20   ⟲ 1.7K   ♡ 11K

Esther Choo MD MPH ✓ @choo_ek · 13 Aug 2017
9/ It's a hell of a hard thing to maintain that level of hate face-to-face.
💬 48   ⟲ 2.1K   ♡ 14K

Esther Choo MD MPH ✓ @choo_ek · 13 Aug 2017
10/ I used to cycle through disbelief, shame, anger. Now I just show compassion and move on. I figure the best thing I can do...
💬 77   ⟲ 1.9K   ♡ 13K

Esther Choo MD MPH ✓ @choo_ek · 13 Aug 2017
...is make sure their hate finds no purchase here. / Fin.
💬 597   ⟲ 2.5K   ♡ 28K

Were you surprised when your tweets on racism in healthcare hit such a nerve?

Even though it was such a grim topic, to know this story resonated and that people were excited to talk about it was uplifting for me and made me feel more energized about initiating conversations about racism and bias, rather than holding back. Nothing that I talk about is a super comfortable conversation. These conversations tend to make people feel defensive. They can become volatile and contentious.

But to me, those tweets were the beginning of a longer conversation about how to support the healthcare workforce. If physicians come from a stronger, better, and safer place, then surely it is going to translate to better and safer patient care.

You were approaching the issue of racism with compassion and a little bit of understanding. I think people appreciated that balance because Twitter can be so polarizing. Everyone seems to be mad all the time.

Twitter is very extreme, and I am not an extreme person. I don't get angry and stomp off. I am the person who stays in the conversation. I stay and stay, and I try to reflect back on what people are thinking. And I wait. If you wait in the conversation long enough, you naturally move toward your common humanity.

I am okay trying to be that someone who brings nuance into a conversation and who appreciates a piece of truth in everyone's opinion. It doesn't matter how different the opinion is from yours, there will always be something that you fundamentally agree on.

You have written that advocacy is a natural part of practicing medicine, and now you're using Twitter as a strong platform for that. Is that something you have always thought? Or has that evolved over the last couple of years?

I came up in a different era. You could be a physician scientist and forget about the rest of world and just take care of the

> I now feel like advocacy has to be part of my job, that it is fulfilling my moral and ethical obligations to my patients.

patient in front of you. There was little expectation for outspoken advocacy. But over the past few years, a switch turned on for me. I now feel like advocacy has to be part of my job, that it is fulfilling my moral and ethical obligations to my patients.

Also, especially as a woman, as you rise through medicine, you start to feel responsible for your peers and for those who are coming behind you. As a woman, you have particular experiences in medicine. When I see trainees, I think, "I don't want you to have the same experiences I had. I don't want you to make the same mistakes I made. I don't want you to grow up in a system in which I struggled in certain ways because of my gender, because of my race." I feel an obligation to my peers, as well as to my patients, and then to my potential patients, which — since I work in the emergency room — is really the entire public.

Do you remember a particular piece of nonsense that somebody told you in your medical education or in your career to discourage you?

Oh, so many things. I am an amazingly unimpressive physical presence. I am about five feet tall, a scrawny, small Asian person with a soft voice. My choice of emergency medicine surprised people. I had a friend in medical school who said, "There is literally nothing *emergency* about you. Emergency is trauma; it's blood, guts, and horror. You are small, and quiet, and kind of reserved. There is nothing about this career that fits you." And I said, "I kind of still want to do it."

I've had people tell me, "Once you have kids, you can't have a high-intensity career." I had my fourth kid, and I was still being told this. Really? You think the fourth one is going to be the one that pushes me over the edge? When you become a parent, people heap tons of negative assumptions on you. It has been fun just blowing past people's expectations and continuing on the path that I saw for myself.

Is that kind of tenacity your superpower?

Not getting discouraged is my advantage. I've always envied people who had a clear natural talent in something. Korean families have a ceremony where they lay all these objects in front of you as a baby. The object you grab is an indication of your talent or your blessings. A brush and you'll be an artist, or a pen and you'll be a scholar, and so on. I think I must not have grabbed anything.

I tried dozens of sports, and I was never good at them. I tried three instruments, and I was never good at them. I was constantly trying things, but there was never anything that I felt like I was born to do. Instead, I latched onto things that I really, really *wanted* to do. Tenacity is what I bring to the table. I will just go, and go, and go after things longer than most people. It turns out that you don't have to be "a natural" to be successful.

You're very good at getting other physicians to share their own stories and join the conversation. Your hashtag #ThisWomanRocks sparked a wave of appreciation for thousands of women in healthcare on Twitter. You seem to be a natural at that.

> I am a product of very supportive communities. This is possible because of social media. I am a symptom. I am a symptom of a completely solid foundation of wonderful people.

You're right, I have to backtrack on my earlier statement: I do have one natural talent. I am very good at seeing the talent in other people. I can see the strength in other people, and I love to draw these strengths out. I want to be a kudos-giver-in-chief, where it is my job to go around saying, "You don't see this in yourself, but it is amazing. Let's shine a light on it so everybody can see it." The #ThisWomanRocks hashtag is very me. It was organic and gave me a lot of joy.

I think we share that enthusiasm for appreciation. I will gladly watch a cardboard box win a lifetime achieve-ment award.

That's exactly it. In medicine, we often experience the opposite. We have "morbidity and mortality conferences." We get notified about every bounce-back patient or bad outcome. There is a steady stream of negative feed-back about your work. Awards and promotions are so rare. In academic medicine, there are generally two promotions your entire career. You can become an associate professor, and then you become a full professor. In between, there is this huge desert with no affirmation or feeling that you are moving forward. My younger brother is a consultant, and he gets promoted every few years. There are all these opportunities for him to be assessed and validated — but not in medicine.

It was heartwarming with #ThisWomanRocks to see people in medicine and science have a chance to celebrate each other.

You've had several other big hashtags on Twitter: #ThatsBias, #DoctorsSpeakOut, and also #ShareaStoryinOneTweet, which was written about in the *New England Journal of Medicine*. What's next for your platform, for putting this community you've built online to work?

> ❝ It has been fun just blowing past people's expectations and continuing on the path that I saw for myself. ❞

That is a good question, and I don't have an answer yet. I am mid-career, and this is the point where the branches open up. Do I want to chair a department? Do I want something that is specific to my specialty? Or do I want to go a different way? I don't know what it is. I have the anticipation of knowing there is a next step for me. I just don't know exactly what it is.

Twitter is a really beautiful thing; it has given me a lot of opportunity to provide information that is shared with a broad audience, and I love it. It is so fun. But it is a small reflection of what I really do. My first official job is doing drug-related and emergency care research. That is my full-time job. My second job is diversity inclusion and equity work.

I started a business called Equity Quotient that gathers analytics on gender equity culture in healthcare organizations.

You need data to create change. If I am taking a mandatory bias class, I need to know that the eight hours I spend there are actually going to change our institution. There have been no metrics for any of this. No measurement of how much microaggression, bias, and discrimination are happening on a day-to-day basis. A friend and I who were both feeling frustrated about healthcare started the company to build those metrics inside institutions.

The existing system in healthcare isn't working for men either. The rates of burnout and suicide are devastating. Why not work to fix it?

It is so true; it isn't working for anybody. All these things tie together. The profession of medicine is bad for women. It is bad for families. It is lacking in compassion and ethical and moral behavior. It has general characteristics that are toxic to really anybody who wants a positive working environment.

We need to fix the house of medicine in many ways. My approach is from a framework of equity and inclusiveness.

What has this community you've built of people working toward equity in healthcare meant to you personally?

Everything I write is a product of the women who support me. I am immersed in a community of women who support me and trigger my brain to think about things. When I write about these things, I get a ton of credit, and those millions of conversations that led to the idea or project are sometimes overlooked.

When I have a byline, there should be this little disclaimer, "Supported by the following network of women." They are my true co-authors, and there are dozens — probably hundreds — of them. I wish I could always cite them, like Dara Kass, who started the group FemInEM.org and Jane van Dis, who is my co-founder of Equity Quotient. I am part of these energizing Facebook groups, like the Physician Moms Group and Physician Women for Democratic Principles.

I am a product of very supportive communities. This is possible because of social media. I am a symptom. I am a symptom of a completely solid foundation of wonderful people. It is hard to capture or name them all, but I am very, very conscious of it. I don't do any of this alone.

All physicians should acknowledge that we have positions of privilege. I can blow past some of these assumptions about myself because I am well-resourced. I have a big support system, my family is very supportive, my husband is very supportive, and we have financial resources so that I can afford help, all so that I can have a high-intensity career.

With the help of that support system, you found the experience of having four kids energizing and productive. It goes against this sense that someone is tapped out after they have a baby. You created a whole human being! Who is to say that you can't work a long shift or start a company?

The narrative is completely messed up. If you have a colleague who is training for a marathon, no one says, "Whoa, you must be useless at work. You are doing this high metabolically draining activity." There are a lot of parallels between training for a marathon and pregnancy. However, if you are training for a marathon, people think you have an increased capacity and commitment. Compare that to doing this incredible, incredible thing of creating another human being and then sustaining them after they are born. It is also physically and metabolically demanding. You are stronger for it and more resilient, but people treat you like you are completely helpless. How is that the narrative? I didn't become helpless, I just proved that I am a badass. ●

"

I didn't become
helpless, I just
proved that I
am a badass.

"

She broke away

Hemalee Patel

DO

Internal medicine physician, entrepreneur, advocate
San Francisco, California

Hemalee Patel is taking a leap. After six years as a hospitalist and clinical instructor at one of the country's top academic health systems, she left to find a new way to practice. She is focusing again on her lifelong passion for lifestyle medicine, prevention, and nutrition. She's in hospital medicine part-time, practicing integrative medicine at a major tech company, and advising health technology investors and startups — all with the goal of making healthcare healthier for herself, her patients, and other providers.

What have you realized from your time outside academic medicine this last year and a half? Do you have a new focus?

I want to bring back the joy in medicine. I want to turn the word "burnout" on its head. I'm thinking a lot about "burning-in." How can we use feelings of frustration and dissatisfaction to change the practice of medicine? I don't want to be a physician who complains and then gets out of the field. I want to be a physician who recognizes how much I love my practice and gets deeper in the field. Even in the short amount of time I've been out of the traditional hospital role, I've been inspired by all the new ways that people are practicing. It can be so much fun to practice medicine. It can be lovely.

Did you feel brave when you decided to leave?

I felt more scared than brave at the time. By leaving that role, I was going against the grain, in a different direction from everyone around me. I feel brave now, though. "I did that! Wow, it was really empowering." By breaking out, I've better realized my self-worth and my professional-worth.

The hospital threw me a nice, very touching going-away party. They made cards with notes about how I had changed the nurses' lives, the practitioners' lives, and pulled in positive patient feedback. I'd never had that before. I wish every physician could have that feeling of being appreciated and knowing you've made a positive impact — without the going-away party.

Were you surprised by how your friends and colleagues reacted to your leaving?

More than a few people called me afterwards to ask "how did you leave? I've always wanted to, I just don't know how." They identify themselves so much in their job and in their institution that they're thinking, "I'm not anything outside of this." Those were really interesting phone calls to take. For me it was a necessity. I had to go.

Was there a specific moment that led you to that choice? Or was it a gradual process?

I felt the "golden handcuffs" phenomenon: lucky to be in a top academic hospital but also stuck. I was working with surgeons in a high-intensity cardiothoracic unit and then a colorectal surgical unit. Many of the patients that I saw had chronic diseases that led them to have major procedures such as open-heart surgeries — diseases that could have been mitigated or prevented if someone helped intervene earlier.

I had wonderful mentors, and the opportunity was awesome, but I started to feel "this isn't necessarily what I set out to do." Every day, I kept battling my own personal values. Is this something that I enjoy? Am I doing what I came to medicine to do? Am I following my true north?

I didn't want to feel like a cog in the wheel. I wasn't fully burned out yet, but I was heading in that direction.

Do you remember when you first heard about burnout? It is seen as an epidemic among physicians today, but it has only fairly recently been openly discussed in healthcare.

One of my mentors, an anesthesiologist who has also now left for a new role, helped create a physician wellness committee. There was a retreat with a cohort of physicians interested in their own wellness, and the first thing they talked about was physician burnout. That was the first time that I heard it being talked about. To hear a professor who had been there for 20 years talking about feeling imposter syndrome, the same thing I was feeling my first year out of residency, it was eye-opening. You realize that a lot of your stressors are similar and that these feelings of isolation and de-personalization are not unique. When you're used to the culture of medicine and so deeply embedded in it, you think that that is how a physician's life should be.

Burnout is a critical issue, but I don't like the term. Your posture changes when you hear it. Burnout is often packaged as something that physicians can't control. An epidemic that is

> **I don't want to be a physician who complains and then gets out of the field. I want to be a physician who recognizes how much I love my practice and gets deeper in the field.**

happening to us, something we need to react to. We have more agency than that. We have the ability to pick something better for us and our patients.

Why do you think breaking away can be so hard for physicians?

Medical training and careers are set up in a way that's reactive. You're *chosen* into medical school, you're *chosen* into residency, you're *chosen* into fellowship, and you're *chosen* into your job. You're reacting to these choices; you're reacting to patients as they come in to see you with health concerns. There's not a lot of space to be proactive. What if more physicians took a step back and said, "How do I want to drive this?" I think it would lead to better satisfaction within the provider community and more longevity in our careers.

"

Burnout is often packaged as something that physicians can't control. An epidemic that is happening to us, something we need to react to. We have more agency than that. We have the ability to pick something better for us and our patients.

"

What were the reasons you pursued a career in medicine in the first place?

I pulled out my personal statement from my application to medical school recently. It was about empowering patients to live their best lives and empowering myself to live my best life so I can help my patients.

I was naïve when I went into medical school. I didn't know the level of competitiveness or the level of self-sacrifice it would take in order to do it. I wanted to learn about nutrition and preventive health, and all around me people were taking their own health for granted, pulling all-nighters constantly, and facing a lot of pressures in terms of substance abuse. We're going into medicine to help people, but we can't even help ourselves.

We invest so much in medical school. We spend years sacrificing our personal life to do something that is selfless. It is tragic when someone realizes that they can't do it anymore. I recently had a surgical resident who was in his fourth year of the surgical residency, with only three years left to go, who said, "I'm so done. I want to leave the field completely." Another colleague called me a few weeks ago almost in tears because he's expected to work 17 nights in a row. He said, "I know that I'm not putting patients first in that instance, and it scares me."

What's your advice to these physicians who are at a tipping point? How do they burn in instead of burn out?

First, see if you can flex down in your current job. Maybe you're tired and taking some time off would help — you have the career security to do that. With a bit of time off, you might get the clarity that, "Wait, no, I actually do want to practice, I just want to practice in this other way." If that doesn't work, there are locum tenens or part-time roles to take while you're figuring something else out. Talk to people in the field who have left medicine entirely because many wish that they still retained some level of patient-facing practice. Maybe it is a function of changing your specialty — physicians do redirect all the time. Figure out what you like to do. What were your hobbies? Do you see alignment with your passions, your personality, and how you can serve in the community as a physician?

For me, it was adding variety that made me feel more vibrant toward my practice. I'm excited, not deflated. There's less certainty in my career, but the variety has helped tremendously. I'm the chair of a health technology advisory board. I'm screening deals at a venture capital firm. I'm on the San Francisco Ballet Auxiliary Board. Having that creativity in my life helps me to be a better physician to my patients.

How do you think this will shake out for your career in the future?

A decade from now, I would love to have a practice where the physicians are taken care of just as well as the patients. Where the physicians get the same type of resources and support that the patients do. How beautiful would that be, when everyone is getting help! We could develop a strong, healing patient-physician experience, the best kind of patient-physician relationship.

There are smart models for clinics where we take care of our physicians in a way that makes them want to stay. It behooves healthcare leaders to think about retention and physician satisfaction — turnover is incredibly expensive. I want a line of physicians outside my practice, trying to work there because I'm taking such good care of my providers. That would be amazing.

Right now, I feel like an entrepreneur — a physician entrepreneur. I'm trying to do something new and create change. When I feel stress, I just take a deep breath and know that I'm following my values.

Why are you so passionate about encouraging physicians to stay in the profession?

By staying in, you can help make medicine what you want it to be. You can lift up everybody else around you, as well. You can burn in and bring up others at the same time.

We have chosen this profession. No one has done this to us. We have chosen to disempower ourselves, being reactionary as

> **"**
> We have chosen to disempower ourselves, being reactionary as physicians, and too often blaming the administrations or the systems around us. We need to empower ourselves again, lean back into the profession of medicine.
> **"**

physicians, and too often blaming the administrations or the systems around us. We need to empower ourselves again, lean back into the profession of medicine.

Take interest in these technologies that are being pushed forward. Get more involved in your institution, your association, and drive the way healthcare is moving. Physicians need to be the drivers of how we want to practice instead of running away from these things. We can help lead the future of medicine. We need to be those leaders. ◢

She found her own orbit

Rhea Seddon

MD

Surgeon, astronaut, medical executive, author, philanthropist
Murfreesboro, Tennessee

Rhea Seddon is not afraid of being first. She was the first woman ever accepted to her general surgery residency program. She was one of the first women in the Astronaut Corps, and she spent 30 days in space on three different NASA Space Shuttle missions. Her marriage was the first astronaut coupling, and their children were the first official "astrotots." She brought leadership and teamwork training from NASA to her work as a healthcare executive, breaking down hospital silos. While it was often difficult to succeed in both of these male-dominated fields, she always made her way.

Were you interested in space and medicine from the very st

I always thought the body was a fascinating thing. That is why I got into medicine. The heart was an amazing thing, the gut was a fascinating, amazing thing, the liver was a scary thing. The lungs were beautiful. I was excited to learn more about the body and figure out what goes wrong with it, how to fix it.

My eighth grade science fair project, in the early 1960s, was about all the terrible things people were predicting could happen to a human if we went to space. You'd be driven mad by the isolation and loneliness. You'd choke on your own saliva. At the time, those first astronauts were test pilots, and test pilots were always men. Space wasn't open to me.

Did people try to discourage you from becoming a physician?

My own childhood pediatrician said, "You're too cute for medical school" and was worried I was going to take a man's place — which was nonsense. I invited him to my medical school graduation, so he saw how that turned out.

At the time, medical schools were accepting about five percent women — it was a man's world. When I became a surgery resident at the University of Tennessee, I was the first and only female. There were days where I just had to go to the bathroom and cry — and then keep going.

As a surgeon, I worked in a hospital where they said women were not allowed in the operating room doctors' lounge. So I sat on a folding chair in the nurses' bathroom. I tried to change the policy but couldn't. So I eventually moved to a hospital with better policies.

Your medical career opened up an opportunity for you to become an astronaut in 1978, the first year the astronaut program accepted women. What was that process like?

NASA was looking for scientists for the Space Shuttle program, and I thought, "Okay, I'm going to apply. There's no point in

and getting excited about it, I'll just apply."
,700 people applied, I thought, "Oh, I'll never
a backup plan; I had a PhD program lined up.
:d me for an interview.
ıe first woman they interviewed. One of the
What would you do if on the plane ride back to
Memphis ıⅽ.. ɔaturday you met the man of your dreams, and he wanted you to stop your career, marry him, and stay home?" I said, "I don't think he'd be the man of my dreams if he wanted me to stop doing what I love doing." The almost all-male selection board looked at their shoes, looked at each other, and we went on with the interview.

I had my private pilot's license, which I'd gotten during my medical training because I thought I was going to be a rich doctor and own an airplane. I was a surgeon, but I had also done research on nutrition in patients undergoing radiation therapy for lung cancer. There was diversity in my background, and I think they liked that. I was very excited I got in; it was what I wanted to do with my life.

You went through a lot of training before you ultimately went to space. Do you remember what you were thinking on that first trip?

It took a number of years to get to space. In the meantime, I got married and had a baby when it became clear it was going to be a while before I would get to fly. I trained, and trained, and trained, and trained for spaceflight. When they finally took me out to the launchpad and strapped me into the Space Shuttle in 1985, I was more excited about finally getting to fly than I was nervous about flying.

The launch is just crazy. You feel like you are sitting on top of an explosion, and then you get going really fast. It took eight and a half minutes to get to orbit. Then the engines cut off, everything was weightless, and you are there. You unstrap and you float around. In your mind, you think you know what it is going to be like, but until you get there, you don't know. It is incredible. It feels like you are in a hot air balloon drifting across the Earth.

“

They didn't teach
leadership in
medical school.
They didn't teach
teamwork in
healthcare.

”

" I said, 'I don't think he'd be the man of my dreams if he wanted me to stop doing what I love doing.' **"**

What stood out to you, looking at Earth from that distance?

The fact that you could watch things evolve. For instance, you could see there were dust storms in Africa, and then when you came around on the next orbit, you would see the dust cloud was now over the Atlantic. Then you'd go another orbit, and you'd say, "Okay, the dust cloud is now over Texas." Feeling this whole planet is interconnected in a way I don't think I had really considered before. Both the landscape and the life on Earth at that altitude were just endlessly fascinating.

That seems like a very consistent theme for you — a fascination with systems. Looking at Earth and the systems of weather and the systems of the body as a surgeon, and the work that you later did as an executive looking at systems in healthcare.

That's an interesting insight, thank you. After I left NASA in 1996, I went to Vanderbilt University Medical Center and talked to the chief medical officer who was thinking about hiring me. He said, "Something you understand that most people in healthcare do not is systems. You are a systems thinker."

You were able to see those two systems up close, healthcare and NASA. Both have been very male-dominated historically, both very scientific. What were the biggest culture differences between healthcare and the space program?

There was a lot of teamwork in the space program. This teamwork approach had been worked out in military aviation and then reinforced during the early space flights. Everybody had to coordinate. There was Mission Control, the flight crew, the people who got you and your spaceship ready — everybody had to work as a team. Everybody *loved* working as a team. They felt an ownership of what was being done, and they were excited about it. All the military people had leadership training.

I noticed these things were very different in medicine. They didn't teach leadership in medical school. They didn't teach teamwork in healthcare. They didn't say, "When you look at the folks in your operating room, you need to know who they are and what they do, and you need to be able to coordinate with them. You have to be able to tell them what you need. You have to find out what they need. You have to be respectful and appreciative." Nobody told me that. I saw doctors who had these huge egos, and they just felt like they were God on Earth. There were some wonderful doctors who were not that way, but overall, the doctors were told, "You are the boss." That doesn't foster teamwork and collaboration.

Did you bring those lessons with you when you went into medical administration at Vanderbilt after NASA?

In 1996 after NASA, I was looking at safety and process improvements at Vanderbilt in Nashville. There were a couple of pilots in the area who had been teaching teamwork to air crews for about 10 years. The aviation field found that airplanes were crashing, not because of mechanical failures, but because of human error. Once the airlines began teaching crews how to work better together, in the 1990s, it became very safe to fly.

Another physician at Vanderbilt had flown with me on one of my Space Shuttle flights, and we decided to work with those pilots to bring their course into our hospital. It was not easy going at first, but I took what I knew and applied it to a different situation, just as I had taken my healthcare background and applied it in my NASA flights. I could take what I learned in aviation and apply it to a different perspective in medicine, resulting in a new way of doing things.

As I look back, space and hospital administration — they were all men's worlds. A lot of my career had to do with persuading men to do things a different way.

Was there a change you were able to implement during your 11 years as assistant chief medical officer at Vanderbilt that stood out as having the biggest positive impact?

Crew resource management, or teamwork training, was well known in aviation at that point, but doctors had never heard of it. I think that was the focus where I had the most impact. We trained more than 5,000 people at Vanderbilt. The program was ultimately so well accepted that we did not have to persuade departments to take the training. They came and asked, "Can our department be next?"

There were outcomes like nurse satisfaction and retention that stood out, too. If you treat people badly and they are not happy, then they are liable to go to another hospital. We were able to say, "Okay, here is actual data that things are better now and people are happier doing their work. They feel like they are part of a team." There were fewer mistakes being made and fewer malpractice claims. It was such a big deal. We took the teamwork training out to the rest of the country, and it has been quite successful.

"

A lot of my career had to do with persuading men to do things a different way.

"

You seem to have this tenacity in your career. Did you always have a plan B?

All the way through. I left NASA because in order to work on a Space Station program, the people in my office with my kind of job had to be willing to go to Russia for two years to train. I had three babies at home and a husband who needed to stay in Houston. I had a plan B ready. I came home and went to work at Vanderbilt. Then when the opportunity came along, I helped form a company, LifeWings, teaching teamwork to healthcare institutions for several years. I handed that over to my partners because I got tired of traveling. That's when I wrote my book *Go For Orbit*, about my husband's and my NASA days. I was always applying something I knew to something different.

Do you have a particular trait that you think has really helped your career?

Probably risk-taking. I was willing to take risks and maybe fail. Persistence, too. To keep trying if I did fail. My book talks about difficulties I had with the NASA training. At five-two, I was the littlest person that NASA had ever taken into the Astronaut Corps, and there were challenges. The worst one for me was the scuba training. I am not a strong swimmer. Really, I'm kind of afraid of the water. I had to do a lot I was not comfortable with. I was just determined to go back the next day and try again.

You have seen so much change in your career, what are you excited about in medicine today?

I'm glad we have more women physicians. They make very good physicians. I have women physicians myself. I think we are lucky that we are now encouraging women to go into the medical field. I think one of the biggest problems is that it is such hard work for so long. I don't know if there is a way around it, but, gosh, it is hard. It is hard when you don't have a supportive spouse. When I went to medical school, all the guys had wives who took care of everything else. I was single. I had to take care of everything else myself. I think women have to be brave to go into medicine, but I am glad they are.

I think women have to be brave to go into medicine, but I am glad they are.

They helped the most vulnerable

Katherine Nammacher

Meredith Hitchcock, MIMS

Co-founders
San Francisco, California

Katherine and Meredith just sold their mental health startup, RideAlong. Their successful exit comes after a three-year sprint, starting with a fellowship at Code for America, taking the company through the prestigious Y Combinator accelerator program, then working independently for a year to grow and scale the business across the country. They designed RideAlong to assist police departments and first responders in safely engaging with people during a mental health or substance abuse crisis. As they prepare for their next steps, the co-founders are looking back at what they learned.

What are lessons you are taking away from your startup experience?

Meredith: I am naturally a risk-averse person. Taking on this startup was the opposite of anything I expected to do. We chose to do a startup on "beast mode" — which was two female co-founders working on mental health in the framework of government technology and particularly law enforcement.

                I logged 75,000 miles of domestic travel for sales calls and conferences this year. I knew nothing about sales before RideAlong; my degrees are in literature and information management, but I came to enjoy it. My approach was basically, "Tell me your problems, and then I'll talk to you about why we think we have some or all of the solution to that." I made some big adjustments in terms of my clothing for the sales role. I was used to wearing sneakers and a shirt. I started wearing dresses. I tried to make myself physically bigger for the meetings with police departments. I got shoulder pads in my blazers. It made me feel more powerful and ready to sell.

Katherine: You were so organized and good at sales. You learned a totally new skill set that you never had before. You went out there, and you did a really good job.

Meredith: Oh, thank you. As startup founders, we learned you have to be slightly above average at a lot of things. We were putting processes in place where there were no processes. Katherine was figuring out how accounting works.

                Aside from learning sales, another big thing for me was public speaking. I'm naturally an introvert. This startup experience gave me the opportunity to present to a number of school groups, particularly to girls of color. It was huge for me because I was interested in computer science in high school. I was the only girl in all my computer classes, though, and opted out of the computer science path before I got to college. Being able to say to them, "I am a black female entrepreneur. There is a model for you. You can do this," was important and powerful to me as somebody who didn't see anyone who looked like me in positions like this.

Katherine:	I learned so much. I learned how to work the spreadsheets. I'm comfortable with cash flows. I mean, I have a bachelor's in fine arts and printmaking. Both of us hit the ground running and kept on going.
	This felt more like a marriage than a business. Meredith is my business partner. We're also good friends. You need to invest in your partner. Whether it is one of us saying something that is not awesome, calling the other and apologizing, "Hey, sorry about that." Or asking, "You're in a weird city by yourself, and you just told me that you had a bad meeting. How are you feeling?" The biggest reason for startups failing is not bad market fit, it's the founding team imploding.

That is so true. I tell my startup clients that companies usually die by suicide, not homicide.

Katherine:	Exactly. Meredith and I have fairly different communication styles, but we work together in a good and positive way. Doing a startup is really, really hard. We've definitely worked 100-hour weeks. I was surprised that other people quickly turned our company into a metaphor for a better and safer future where policing is more empathetic. It wasn't just our friends, it was police chiefs promoting our approach to other police chiefs, saying, "I really believe in this, and we should do this in our county."

Meredith:	Another thing I learned because of the startup is how much mental health is stigmatized in the U.S. and how many people are affected by it. We would talk to an investor or a cop, or somebody at a conference about RideAlong, and they would quickly confide in us and say, "My brother was affected." or "I have a cousin with schizophrenia." There was something wonderful about inadvertently creating a space for people to acknowledge something that is very painful for them, something they do not usually talk about.

It's October 2018, tell me about your startup journey coming to an end. You have a successful exit, selling the company so that

"

Being able to say to them, "I am a black female entrepreneur. There is a model for you. You can do this," was important and powerful to me as somebody who didn't see anyone who looked like me in positions like this.

> Mental health is obviously a health issue, not a policing issue, but police are the ones who show up.

it can scale faster with this larger organization, but it still seems emotional for all this work to be wrapping up. How are you feeling?

Katherine: It is intense. We're being acquired by a company working in our space called OpenLattice. We have full confidence that they're going to be continuing our work and serving our clients. We built something that is going to live after us in a real and immediate way. Now we are giving what we've built to someone else. It is both a separation and grieving process.

Meredith: It's a very, very strange emotional process. Things that I didn't expect to be emotional are emotional...like documentation. I suddenly have a lot of time to think about all my feelings around this large transition. We're getting off "beast mode."

How does RideAlong help improve those frequent mental health interactions in policing?

Katherine: As an officer is headed to a 911 call, they search the person's name or the address where they're going. With RideAlong, a response plan is available inside their system with crucial information organized to be quickly available as they are headed to the call, including de-escalation techniques, officer safety information, and what behaviors to expect. They can use the tool to see what to do after things have calmed down at the location, and also important contact information related to the person, and past interactions.

Meredith: First responders can break the cycle. Our app delivers information that helps resolve a 911 call effectively by bringing people in crisis to better diversion options. Without this information, officers confronted with a behavioral health situation have three options: arrest the person if there is a crime, take the person to the hospital if it seems like they are an immediate danger to themselves or others, or leave them there. With our app, the officer knows instead, for example, that they should call the building manager at supportive housing and have the manager talk to the individual — rather than sending the person in crisis to the ER, having them walk out of the ER because they don't qualify for the 72-hour hold, having the person call 911 again the next day, and then going through the whole process again.

How did you develop the concept for RideAlong?

Meredith: Most people have a particular idea of policing that is formed by television. It's kicking in doors, and it's chasing bad guys. In 2016, Katherine and I were part of the safety and justice track with Code for America and partnered with the Seattle Police Department. We saw that in the day-to-day, in our research interviews, and our ride-alongs, there is a lot of community caretaking by the police. It is estimated that 10 percent of 911 calls involve mental health. If you talk to literally any police department — and we've talked to hundreds now — they will estimate that it is actually between 25 percent and 35 percent of their calls. Mental health is obviously a health issue, not a policing issue, but police are the ones who show up.

Was there some culture shock initially working with first responders?

Meredith: There was an adjustment moving from Silicon Valley culture, where companies pride themselves on being non-hierarchical and flat, to the culture of law enforcement, which is one of the most hierarchical organizations you can encounter. Code for America helped us prepare for some of that adjustment, trying to manage the dynamics between lieutenant, sergeant, and officer. I remember we once asked a firefighter what his biggest challenge was, and he started shouting for five minutes. We're just sitting there looking around in the break room, and I was thinking, "Oh no. What have we done? What's happening?" Then one of the other firefighters intervened, and he calmed down and said, "Sorry, I'm not mad at you. It's just that nobody's ever asked me before."

How did you build trust in a situation like that, where you were very much outsiders?

Katherine: We were 27 years old when we were first starting our startup journey. A member of our team, Grace, was 23 and had a purple mohawk. We showed up to a police department command staff where the youngest person was 45 or 50. We were literally the age of their children. Code for America does a very smart thing where they get a couple of pieces of information about the project from the government partner early and then have your team do a small prototype to bring when you first meet. We showed the Seattle Police Department a prototype, and it changed the entire conversation. It immediately changed the perception of us from being young technologists and young adults to very capable colleagues in a way that I didn't even realize until later.

Were you able to demonstrate the positive impact on the community as a result of your work?

Katherine: In July 2018, we did a study of 220 people who had at least six months of post-intervention data. This gave us a look at the application at work in Seattle, where 323 people (about three percent of Seattle's total 911 callers per year) have RideAlong profiles from either being frequent 911 users or because of the gravity of their calls. We tracked a 35 percent decrease in the number of 911 calls involving those individuals over six months.

"

Walk into
conversations
with partners
who are truly
different from
you. Leave your
ego at the door
and just listen.

"

We found positive changes in numbers of involuntary psychiatric referrals, numbers of arrests, and uses of force. The total deferred cost for the Seattle Police Department and King County was $407,000 over just six months. To be totally frank, it was a phenomenal surprise. You put something out there, you hear from people that the technology is working, but it is incredible to see that listening to the community resulted in massive cost savings, as well as massive safety improvements for citizens and officers.

Meredith: I remember one roll call meeting we attended when an officer stood up in front of his squad totally unprompted and said, "I used this app in the field. This really works. You should give it a shot." To have an officer vouch for us was a huge moment of buy-in. People do see the value; they are willing to go to bat for us. That moment was one of the turning points for me in terms of having built something that has the ability to make a difference for vulnerable people.

What's the biggest takeaway from your startup experience? What should other people know who are starting up a company to address problems in healthcare?

Katherine: People underestimate how much a difference small improvements can make. There is so much low-hanging fruit out there.

> ## Healthcare means a lot of things; it looks like a lot of different things.

Sit down and listen and build empathy and think about a solution collaboratively. Walk into conversations with partners who are truly different from you. Leave your ego at the door and just listen.

Meredith: Healthcare means a lot of things; it looks like a lot of different things. For example, the huge overlap between policing and mental health is surprising to a lot of people. Housing is also healthcare. It is hard for someone to stabilize a leg wound when they don't have a clean place to sleep at night. I tried to fight being overwhelmed by the size of the problem and how connected everything seemed. I'd ask myself, "How do we know that we're doing enough and that the problem we're tackling is large enough?" Fixing one problem really well and then moving on from there is a good place to start.

Also, I'm taking away the lesson of "you can survive it." You will survive. Even if you don't have any idea what you're doing, you will figure out a way. You will figure out who to ask. You will learn how to do the thing well enough to get by. As a risk-averse person — knowing I will figure it out reduces my fear of the startup process.

Katherine: I would do it again.

Meredith: Yeah. I would do it again, too. ◢

Next Steps

We're at a stopping point with this volume, but the work doesn't stop. Are you ready to speak out? To start something new? What problems do you want to solve? What kind of healthcare future can we create together? (I did warn you in the introduction that I'm relentless.)

Make no mistake, this isn't easy. Standing up for yourself is a good first step, but major change only comes when we stand up for each other. We can't remake medicine alone.

We need to talk to each other about problems we face, push each other to be brave, bring in diverse voices, and consider the most vulnerable. We need to speak up for each other when we see something unfair. When I think about the women in *Procedure*, they collectively seem to be working toward four simple and very impactful things:

Fairness. A better healthcare system is more fair in how we pay for it, how we research new drugs, how we treat people, and how we invest in new ideas. Transparency is a crucial first step here. We need the data to change what isn't working.

Kindness. The desire to care for people is what brought so many of us to this sector, but this drive can get worn down along the way. The women in this book have shown the power of making choices that are generous, balanced, and mindful for both patients and providers.

Collaboration. Women tend to be more collaborative leaders, and the call for teamwork is consistent in this book. We're not alone out here. Listen more, lean on each other, share information, and build communities.

Bravery. Nothing changes until someone is willing to speak up, be the first, and bring up others with them. Together, we can shake off the status quo and try new things for our healthcare system as a whole.

These are reasonable things to ask for. They're four things that are hard to disagree with, no matter where you stand. These values in action could help us realize a more affordable, effective, and humane healthcare system for everyone. Do they spark something in you? Are you ready to help?

One voice at a time. One act of bravery. One new idea launched into the world. Each of us, together, working for something better. This is how we remake medicine.

— **Emily F. Peters**

Conversation Starter

We are thrilled for this book to spark conversations about remaking medicine in your book clubs, women's groups, and classes. Let's help lift each other up. Here are a few study guide questions to encourage your discussion:

Which profile do you identify with most closely? What is it about her that you recognize in yourself?

How does reading these profiles make you feel about the healthcare sector? In the past? In the future?

Did you find any parts of this book controversial or challenging to the way you view women in the healthcare sector?

What should be the responsibility of men in healthcare to help make things more equitable? Do you have a positive or negative story to share?

What part of healthcare do you feel is hardest to change? Why?

What non-traditional roles or paths do you think women could take to create change in healthcare?

What do you think are effective ways to navigate around organizational blocks? How about navigating personal self-limiting beliefs?

Which of the situations in this book have you had personal experience with?

What is something you're proud of standing up for or helping to change in healthcare?

What do these stories inspire you to do?

Notes